Usborne Workbo

Comprehension

This book belongs to

POPPY Esme

There are answers on page 26, and notes
for grown-ups at the back of the book.

The jungle animals are going to practise their comprehension skills. Can you help them? First, use a pen or pencil to trace over their names on these labels.

Crock

Tan-tan

Cheeky

Lem

Ant

Froggy

Write a name for the mouse here:

Can you think of a name for me? Remember to start with a capital letter.

_____

Usborne Workbooks
Comprehension

Illustrated by Marta Cabrol

Written by Caroline Young
Designed by Meg Dobbie

Baz

Tig

Lep

Beaky

There are extra pages for more practice at the back of the book.

Edited by Kristie Pickersgill
Series Editor: Felicity Brooks
With thanks to Alice Morrison-Lebbon

Lists and labels

Cheeky's bedroom is in a mess. Her toys and shoes are everywhere!
Can you write the correct word on each label in her room to show her
where everything goes? Choose from the words below.

Toys   Shoes   Books   Shorts   Dresses

Thanks!
I can tidy
up now.

Cheeky

Cheeky has found four things she doesn't need any more, so she's going to take them to the jungle charity shop. Choose the correct words from the box below to write on each label.

train set   baby toy   picture book   t-shirt

Can you think of some toys you played with when you were small, but don't play with any more? Write a list of them in this box.

If you can't remember your old toys, write some toys young children often play with.

My old toys

_____

_____

_____

_____

_____

Now write a list of four things you think you'll always keep.

_____   _____

_____   _____

I am definitely keeping this teddy forever.

What did we do?

Froggy and Crock went swimming yesterday. Froggy has written four sentences about it, and Crock has drawn four pictures. Look at the orange strip below. Choose the correct sentence to write under each picture.

We were really hungry afterwards.
We put on our swimsuits.

It was fun to splash in the water.
It was a warm, sunny morning.

_____

_____

_____

_____

_____

_____

_____

_____

What did you do yesterday? Write a sentence about it here.

_____

What do you wish you had done yesterday?

I wish I'd gone swimming too!

_____

Tig

The animals eat four meals a day: breakfast, lunch, dinner and supper. Tig's written a diary of what he did between his meals yesterday, but he's put his sentences in the wrong order. Draw lines to join the pictures with the right sentences.

Monday

That was a busy day, Tig.

Tan-tan

I bet you ate the cake as well.

I played the trumpet after dinner.

I read my book after lunch.

Before supper, I baked a cake.

After breakfast, I played football.

Lep

Can you circle the names of all Tig's meals in his list?
Now, write one of them in each gap below, but remember to choose carefully.

In the jungle, the animals eat _____ early.

In the middle of the day, they eat a very big _____ .

In the afternoons they rest, before thinking about what to eat for

_____ . Before bed, they have some _____ .

Which meal of the day do you like best? _____

Story ideas

Baz loved listening to stories when he was a cub. Now, he enjoys writing them, too. He often changes a story he already knows. Circle what he's changed in this story about three bears.

One day, three bears went ice-skating. When they got home, someone had eaten their sandwiches, and was fast asleep on their sofa. It was a young boy! He was very scared, and really hungry, so the bears invited him to stay for tea.

The plot of the real story is on page 32.

Can you answer these three questions about Baz's story using full sentences? The first one has been done for you.

1. Where did the bears go? <u>The bears went ice-skating.</u>

2. What did the boy eat? _____

3. What happened next? _____

_____

From the list below, circle three words that you think describe how the boy might feel. Then, draw a line under words that might describe the bears' feelings.

scared   cross   sorry   angry   terrified   nervous   guilty   worried

Tan-tan sometimes finds it hard to finish her stories. Here's a story she started today. Read it through and then help her choose an ending.

A young orangutan called Min-min set out to find her favourite fruit. It only grew in one place on one tree in the heart of the jungle. When she reached the spot, a hungry leopard was there, licking its lips.

What should Min-min do? Choose one of these three ways of finishing the story.

1. Min-min gives up and goes home.

2. She quickly climbs up and picks the fruit.

3. She hides, and waits until the leopard goes away.

Write an ending for the story here, starting after Tan-tan's last sentence. Make it as exciting and dramatic as you can.

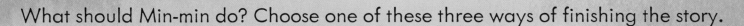

_____

_____

_____

Can you think of a different ending for the story?

You could write it on the blank pages at the back of the book.

What do I do?

Ant has promised to make sandwiches for lunch, but he's in a terrible muddle. Everyone's chosen a different sandwich filling!

Why can't they all have ant sandwiches, like me?

Ant

I would like a cheese sandwich please.

Definitely egg.

Peanut butter for me.

Banana, of course.

Now Ant is so confused, he's forgotten how to make a sandwich. Can you put these instructions in order by writing 1, 2, 3 or 4 in each box?

Remember, instructions tell you how to do something.

☐ Place the second slice on top.

☐ Cut the sandwich in half. Enjoy!

☐ Spread butter on two slices of bread.

☐ Put some of the filling onto one slice.

Delicious sandwiches! Thanks, Ant.

There's fresh fruit salad for dessert, but Ant isn't sure how to prepare the fruit. Look at these pictures, and write some simple instructions under each one. The first one has been done for you.

You'll need these words: **peel slice chop mix**

Be very careful with that knife!

1. Peel and slice a banana.

2. _____

My favourite dessert! Thanks, Ant.

pineapple

3. _____

4. _____

Ant is a much more confident cook now, and wants to do more cooking. Draw a line to link each of these foods with how he could prepare them.

bread	onion	potato	egg	cream
mash	toast	boil	fry	whip

Instructions must always be clear, and easy to understand. Numbering each step can help.

Tell me about it

Beaky has gone to the library to find out what other birds live in the jungle, but there are so many books about birds! Put a tick under the book he needs.

Beaky

Birds of **Prey**

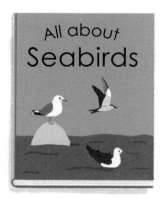

All about **Seabirds**

A Big Book of **Jungle Birds**

○   ○   ○

Can you join a description of each jungle bird to the right picture? The first one has been done for you.

These birds have big, bright crests of feathers on their heads.

This bird's body is black and white. Its neck curls over its chest.

This bird has a red and white head and blue, yellow and green wings.

Scarlet macaw

Cock-of-the-rock

King vulture

Do you have a favourite bird? How would you describe it? Use some of the words on this page if you like.

_____

_____

In the library, Beaky has found a book about jungle animals.
Draw a line to match the description with the correct animal.

Jungle animals

Jaguar

Frog

Orangutan

Hmm, some of these look familiar...

This animal spends some of its time in water and some on land.

This animal has sharp teeth, spotted fur and is very good at hiding.

This furry animal is a very good climber and likes eating fruit.

How would you describe Baz the bear? Write your description here.

Big and hairy?

Tall, dark and handsome, perhaps?

How would you describe yourself?

You could write a description of yourself, or a friend, on page 30.

What's happening?

Lep, Tig and Ant are reading a book about a voyage on a sailing boat. Read the story, then help them answer some questions about it. The first one has been done for you.

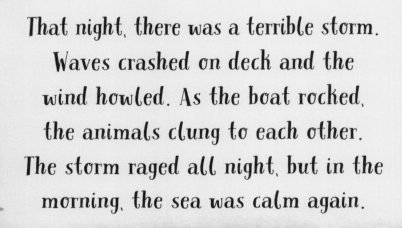

> That night, there was a terrible storm. Waves crashed on deck and the wind howled. As the boat rocked, the animals clung to each other. The storm raged all night, but in the morning, the sea was calm again.

1. What was the weather like that night?

The weather was very stormy.

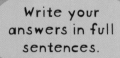

Write your answers in full sentences.

2. What did the animals do?

_____

3. How long did the storm last?

_____

Circle any words in the story that help you imagine the storm.

There's no right or wrong answer, so don't worry.

In the next chapter, the boat arrives at an island, and the animals go ashore.

If you landed on the island, how would you feel? Write about it here, using some of these words if you like.

There's more writing space at the back of the book if you need it.

sand	explore	jungle	beach	excited
interested	nervous	sunny	curious	safe

_____

_____

_____

_____

_____

Now imagine you're going on a journey. It might be over a scorching desert or up snowy mountain peaks. You can write about it on page 31, if you like.

Stories, which are made up, are called fiction. Plays and poems are different kinds of fiction, too.

Poetry practice

Cheeky and Beaky are writing poems. First, they write ones that rhyme, which means some of the words sound like each other. Circle two words that rhyme in this sentence.

The tall trees swayed in the breeze.

Cheeky has written a rhyming poem about pizza, which she loves. Draw lines between the pairs of words that rhyme.

Thin and crispy, topped with herbs and spices

I bet I can eat five or six big slices.

Tomatoes, olives, mushrooms and lots of cheese

Ooh, can I have the last slice, please?

Write one of these words in each gap in this poem to find out what food Beaky likes best.

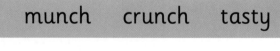

munch   crunch   tasty

You'll have to guess the last word, of course.

Every day, I like to _____ them,

Red or green, I love to _____ them,

Nice and juicy, crisp and _____,

Give me an _____, not a sugary pastry.

Not all poems have rhymes, but every word is important. Here's Cheeky's poem about the jungle. Circle the parts you like best.

Thick trees block the sun and
Leaves rustle in the warm breeze.
High up, hidden in the green
Hundreds of eyes peep.

Remember that each line of a poem starts with a capital letter.

Can you write a poem here about somewhere special to you? It might be your home, or somewhere you went on a trip. Before you begin, write a list of some good words to use.

Good words

_____
_____
_____
_____
_____
_____
_____

I really like the word 'chunky'.

I'm a fan of 'rippling', myself.

It's a good idea to keep a list of words you really like. You never know when you might use them.

18

Party plans

The animals are organizing a birthday party for Tan-tan. Here's a list of the party food they'd like. Write each thing on the menu as neatly as you can.

Tan-tan

sandwiches   cakes   crisps   grapes   biscuits   ice cream   pizza

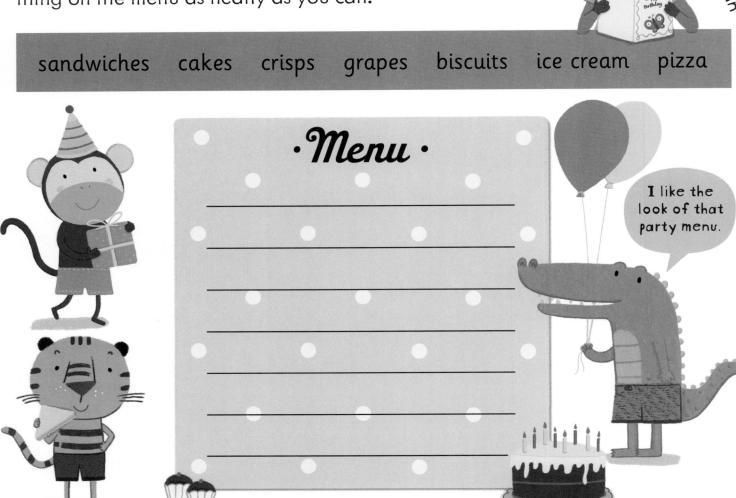

• Menu •

I like the look of that party menu.

Froggy wants everyone to play musical chairs, but she always gets mixed up when she explains the game. She's written the rules down, but can you put them in the right order, by writing 1, 2, 3 or 4 in each box?

☐ When the music stops, the animals must sit on a chair.

☐ The music plays and everyone dances.

☐ The last animal left sitting on a chair is the winner.

☐ Anyone without a chair to sit on is out.

Lep is in charge of giving out bags of little gifts at the end of the party. What should she put inside them? Choose three things and circle them.

If you could add one more gift, what would it be? It can be anything at all, as long as it fits in the bag. Write it here: _____

If you were planning a party, what would it be like? Write about it below. (Use the blank pages at the back of the book if you need more space.)

That sounds like a great party!

_____
_____
_____
_____
_____
_____
_____
_____

What do you think?

Tan-tan has some birthday money, but she can't decide what to spend it on. Here are the adverts for three things she really likes. Circle the one you think she should choose.

You need a hat like this!

Decorated with jungle flowers and bright bows, each one is different.

Come to our Restaurant

Enjoy the most delicious food in the jungle. Tasty, healthy and filling.

Visit our AMAZING ADVENTURE PLAYGROUND

Swing from our rope ladders and walk across stunning treetop bridges. You'll love it!

Adverts like these are trying to persuade you to buy or do something.

Now, circle the words or phrases on the adverts that might persuade you.

The phrase 'tasty, healthy and filling' made me feel hungry.

I think I really do need a hat like that.

Crock has started a blog to encourage people to visit the jungle. Add one of the words from this box in each gap.

Choose the words you think sound best.

sparkling   crashing   colourful   friendly   dazzling
lovely   smiling   beautiful   best   prettiest

We have _____ waterfalls, _____ flowers and

_____ animals here in the jungle. The weather

is _____ and everyone is _____.

The jungle is simply the _____ place in the world.

Ant and Tig aren't happy. They want to change Crock's blog.

Fill in the gaps below so that the jungle sounds awful. You could use some of these words.

Too many people will come to the jungle.

Yes. It will be too crowded.

dangerous   horrible   poisonous
scary   nasty   fierce   hot
miserable   sweaty   worst

We have _____ waterfalls, _____ flowers and

_____ animals here in the jungle. The weather

is _____ and everyone is _____.

The jungle is simply the _____ place in the world.

Changing a few words can really change a piece of writing, can't it? Always choose the words you use carefully.

Plots and stories

It's rainy today, so the animals are reading old story books, but raindrops have smudged the pages. Write one of these three phrases in each gap. You'll probably have heard them all before.

A phrase is a small group of words.

Once upon a time   who is the fairest of them all   lived happily ever after

Lep is reading **Sleeping Beauty.**

_____,

a beautiful princess lay sleeping, under a spell.

Ant is reading **Snow White.**

Mirror, mirror on the wall, _____

_____?

Tig is reading **Red Riding Hood.**

The Wolf was dead, Granny was safe, so everyone

_____.

Aww, I do love a happy ending.

What stories do you enjoy reading?
Write the titles of three you like.

I like those stories too.

1. _____

2. _____

3. _____

Can you make up a story, using three things from
the stories you listed above?

Which characters would you choose?

_____

_____

I would have
Prince Charming
riding a dragon to
rescue Rapunzel
from her tower.

In my story, the
Fairy Godmother
and the Three Little
Pigs would go to a
giant's castle.

Where would the story be set?

_____

What would happen in it?

_____

_____

_____

_____

You can use the space on pages 28 and 29 to write your story out.

Comprehension quiz

You've helped the animals do lots of comprehension activities in this book. See if you can do this quiz, and become a comprehension expert!

1. Which word goes where?
Write the correct word on each label.

| book | clock | toy robot | football |

2. Crock's going shopping. Put a tick in the box next to three things he needs to buy for a party.

☐ a) balloons   ☐ b) shampoo   ☐ c) crisps

☐ d) magazine   ☐ e) cake   ☐ f) buttons

3. Lep's written some instructions for Tig to paint a wall in his house, but they're muddled up. Put 1, 2, 3 or 4 next to each of these steps, so that it makes sense.

☐ Paint the wall with a paintbrush.

☐ Cover the floor to protect it.

☐ Open the tin of paint.

☐ Clear all the furniture away.

4. Answer these questions about this part of an adventure story. Use full sentences if you can.

> The pirates went ashore at dawn.
> They looked at their map and went
> to the spot marked with an 'X'.
> Then, they started to dig. Three hours
> later, they found the buried treasure.

a) When did the pirates go ashore? _____

b) Where did they dig? _____

c) How long did they dig for? _____

5. Underline two words you think might describe the pirates' feelings when they found the treasure. There's no right answer, so don't worry.

bored	excited	happy
nervous	relieved	disappointed

6. Circle the words that rhyme with each other and join them with a line.

The jungle is so quiet at night.

Hidden in the darkness we sleep, out of sight.

The only sounds are the breeze in the trees

And the flap and squeak of bats.

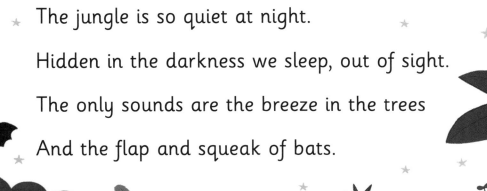

Quiz answers

1.  clock  toy robot  book  football

2. a) balloons   c) crisps   e) cake

3. 1. Clear all the furniture away.   2. Cover the floor to protect it.
   3. Open the tin of paint.   4. Paint the wall with a paintbrush.

4. a) They went ashore at dawn.   b) They dug at the spot marked with an X
   c) They dug for three hours.   on the map.

6.
The jungle is so quiet at (night)

Hidden in the darkness we sleep, out of (sight.)

The only sounds are the (breeze) in the (trees)

And the flap and squeak of bats.   (1 point for each rhyming pair.)

Score 1 point for each correct answer and write your score in this box: **16**

Answers

Pages 4-5

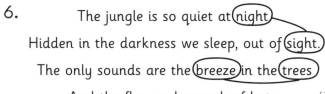

Dresses

Shoes

Shorts

Books

Toys

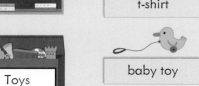

t-shirt

baby toy

train set

picture book

Pages 6-7

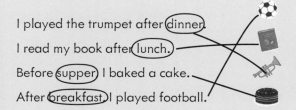

It was a warm, sunny morning

We put on our swimsuits.

It was fun to splash in the water.

We were really hungry afterwards.

I played the trumpet after (dinner)

I read my book after (lunch.)

Before (supper) I baked a cake.

After (breakfast) I played football.'

In the jungle, the animals eat **breakfast** early. In the middle of the day, they eat a very big **lunch.** In the afternoons they rest, before thinking about what to eat for **dinner.** Before bed, they have some **supper.**

Pages 8-9

One day, three bears went (ice-skating) When they got home, someone had eaten their (sandwiches,) and was fast asleep on their (sofa.) It was a young (boy!) He was very scared, and really hungry, so the bears (invited him to stay for tea.)

2. The boy ate their sandwiches
3. The bears invited him to stay for tea.

Here are some of the words you could have chosen:
(scared) cross (sorry) angry terrified nervous (guilty) worried

This is one way you could have joined the words.

bread	onion	potato	egg	cream
mash	toast	boil	fry	whip

Pages 10-11

3 Place the second slice on top.
4 Cut the sandwich in half. Enjoy!
1 Spread butter on two slices of bread.
2 Put some of the filling onto one slice.

1. Peel and slice a banana.
2. Peel and chop (or slice) an apple.
3. Peel and chop a pineapple.
4. Mix together in a bowl.

Pages 12-13

A Big Book of **Jungle Birds**

These birds have big, bright crests of feathers on their heads.

This bird's body is black and white. Its neck curls over its chest.

This bird has a red and white head and blue, yellow and green wings.

This animal spends some of its time in water and some on land.

This animal has sharp teeth, spotted fur and is very good at hiding.

This furry animal is a very good climber and likes eating fruit.

Pages 14-15

2. The animals clung to each other.   3. The storm lasted all night.

Pages 16-17

The tall (trees) swayed in the (breeze.)

Thin and crispy, topped with herbs and spices
I bet I can eat five or six big slices.
Tomatoes, olives, mushrooms and lots of cheese
Ooh, can I have the last slice, please?

Every day, I like to **munch** them,
Red or green, I love to **crunch** them,
Nice and juicy, crisp and **tasty**,
Give me an **apple**, not a sugary pastry.

Pages 18-19

2 When the music stops, the animals must sit on a chair.
4 The last animal left sitting on a chair is the winner.
1 The music plays and everyone dances.
3 Anyone without a chair to sit on is out.

Pages 20-21

Here are some of the words and phrases you could have chosen:

You need a hat like this!
Decorated with jungle flowers and bright bows, each one is different

Come to our Restaurant
Enjoy the most delicious food in the jungle. Tasty, healthy and filling.

Visit our AMAZING ADVENTURE PLAYGROUND
Swing from our rope ladders and walk across stunning treetop bridges. You'll love it!

Pages 22-23

Once upon a time, a beautiful princess lay sleeping, under a spell.

Mirror, mirror on the wall, who is the fairest of them all?

The Wolf was dead, Granny was safe, so everyone lived happily ever after.

28

You can use these
pages to practise your
writing skills.

Ant has a long, pointy nose and a big bushy tail. He loves swimming and walking in the forest.

Write a description of yourself, or a friend, on this page.

Think about travelling to a faraway place and describe your journey on this page.

What did you do, see, think and feel?

Goldilocks and the Three Bears

A little girl called Goldilocks finds a cottage in the woods. She breaks one of three chairs in it, eats one of the three bowls of porridge and falls asleep on one of the three beds. When the bears return, she runs away.

Checklist

Put a tick next to each of the comprehension activities in this book when you've done them. What a lot you've learnt!

☐ Writing lists and labels (pages 4–5)

☐ Putting steps in order (pages 6–7)

☐ Changing stories (pages 8–9)

☐ Writing instructions (pages 10–11)

☐ Looking for information (pages 12–13)

☐ Answering questions (pages 14–15)

☐ Writing poems (pages 16–17)

☐ Planning a party (pages 18–19)

☐ Persuasive writing (pages 20–21)

☐ Well-known stories (pages 22–23)

Notes for grown-ups

Comprehension is taught in a wide variety of ways in schools, but all of them aim to increase children's confidence in reading, hearing and interpreting text. This book has a selection of activities, including answering questions on a piece of text, writing clear instructions, making lists, writing labels and analysing how language can be used persuasively.

The best way of building children's confidence in comprehension is to encourage them to read widely, to ask questions about what they discover and to be inspired by the huge choice of words, and written styles, available to them. Comprehension, in its truest sense, is 'understanding', and this book aims to help children understand how language works, and learn how to use it well in lots of different contexts.